The KnowHow Book of
DETECTION

TIGER BOOKS INTERNATIONAL
LONDON

T11739

First published in 1978
by Usborne Publishing Ltd
Usborne House
83-85 Saffron Hill, London EC1 8RT

©Usborne Publishing Ltd 1990, 1978

Printed in Italy

This edition published in 1997
by Tiger Books International
PLC, Twickenhan

ISBN 1-85501-882-9

Lettering By J.G. McPherson

MEET SHAMUS

THIS IS DETECTIVE INSPECTOR SHAMUS, HEAD OF FUZZVILLE C.I.D. (CRIMINAL INVESTIGATION DEPARTMENT). HIS LEGENDARY PATIENCE, KNOWLEDGE OF CRIME AND CRIMINALS, AND KEEN EYE FOR DETAIL ARE THE KEYS TO HIS SUCCESS.

OLD BILL...

THIS IS DETECTIVE CONSTABLE WILLIAM WATSON ('OLD BILL'). HE HAS JUST HUNG UP HIS HELMET TO JOIN THE C.I.D. AS A DETECTIVE. HIS OVER-ENTHUSIASM SOMETIMES LEADS TO DISASTER...

AND THE FLAT MAN

THIS IS WEEDY WEEKY— KNOWN AS 'THE FLAT MAN' TO POLICE OF A DOZEN COUNTRIES. USUALLY HE WORKS ALONE BUT THIS TIME HE SEEMS TO HAVE AN ACCOMPLICE... A PARTNER IN CRIME.

READ THEIR STORY TO WATCH A DETECTIVE TEAM AT WORK...AND LEARN HOW TO FOLLOW IN THEIR FOOTSTEPS.

How to Use This Book

A good detective needs special skills, lots of training—and imagination. In this book there is a mystery story to test your imagination. There are also puzzles to solve and projects to teach you skills, like finding a get away car.

Try some of the puzzles as you read the story. See if you can solve the mystery Shamus faces on page 27. Then go back and try the projects.

As you know, a detective is a plain-clothes policeman. After becoming a detective he wears no uniform and works only on solving crimes.

But before this he may spend years as a patrolman— directing traffic, walking his beat, and helping ordinary people in emergencies. This is how he learns to be observant, to think logically, and to keep cool in emergencies.

It takes experience to learn these things, but there are special skills that help a lot. In this book we have given you some tips on these, too.

Our story is set in England, but detective work is very much the same in every country. All over the world the police co-operate—as you can see when you read about Interpol. The fight against crime is international.

The KnowHow Book of Detection

Judy Hindley
and
Donald Rumbelow
(City of London Police
Chairman, British Crime Writers Association, 1978)

Illustrated by Colin King

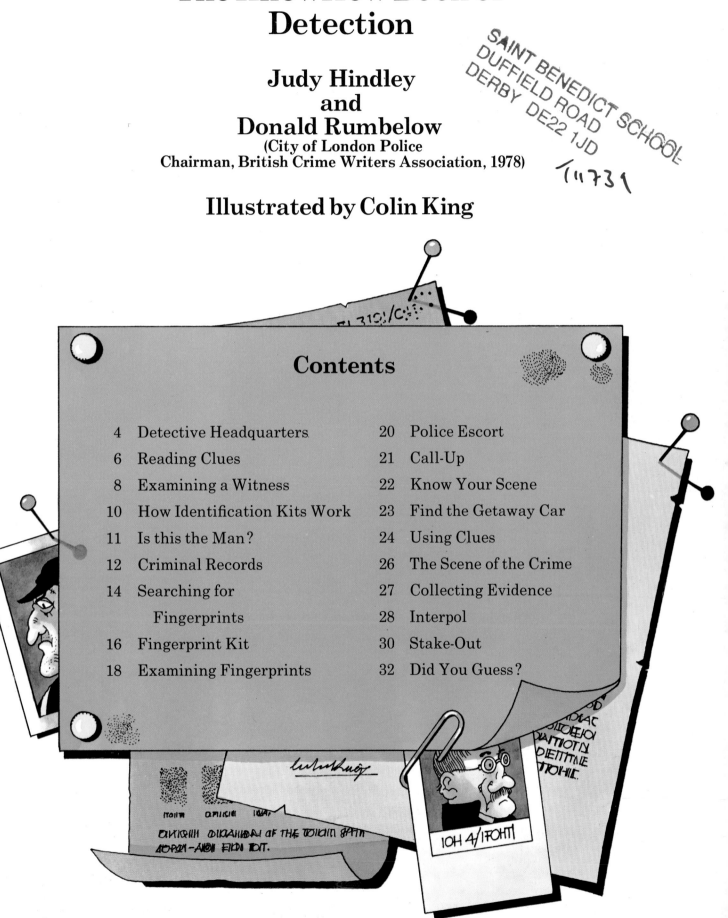

Contents

Detective Headquarters

As a detective, the first thing you must do is set up headquarters (H.Q.). This is where you will keep your reports, your criminal records, your maps of the neighbourhood—all the information you will need in order to act quickly when the time is ripe.

A good detective needs a lot of information. He may spend hours walking slowly round his neighbourhood, getting to know his ground. But he spends even more time at his desk at H.Q., sifting through reports and carefully piecing together tiny facts and clues.

His office may look dusty (police stations never close) but his paperwork must always be in perfect order. He may have twenty cases going at once and he may get new information on any of them. He must be sure each new report is added. Information is his chief weapon in the battle against crime.

Look around the picture on the right to see what you need to set up headquarters. Below you can see the first thing you need—a warrant card.

Warrant Card

A warrant card is a policeman's identity card.

THIS IS FUZZVILLE H.Q.— IT'S BEEN A SLOW DAY— AND DETECTIVE-INSPECTOR SHAMUS IS GETTING RESTLESS.

SHAMUS

BOX FILE

NOTEBOOK

DESK DIARY

IT'S JUST TOO QUIET, BILL. ALL THE VILLAINS SEEM TO HAVE GONE UNDERGROUND ...OR STRAIGHT. I DON'T KNOW WHAT TO MAKE OF IT!

NOT EVEN AN ESCAPED MOUSE IN SIGHT

WARRANT CARD

BACK VIEW

TAPE

PIN

Making a Warrant Card

Cut out a neat piece of white cardboard (or cereal packet with white paper glued over it). Glue on to it a good head-and-shoulders photograph of yourself. Print on it your name and the words 'Warrant Card' and sign it in ink.

If possible, cover the card with see-through plastic. Stick a safety pin on the back with sticky tape and pin it behind your lapel. Then you can flip back your lapel and show it to identify yourself.

Box File

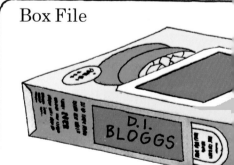

D.I. BLOGGS

A box file is just a handy container for information on the cases you are investigating. Use it to carry things like photographs, reports and statements made by witnesses.

DIVISIONAL MAP

BILL

MISSING PERSONS

CRIMINAL RECORDS A/Z

POLICE GAZETTES

STOLEN VEHICLES

SUSPECTS CONVICTIONS

LOST PROPERTY

CRIMINAL RECORDS FILING CABINET

REPORTS

COULD BE WE'VE SORTED 'EM OUT, GUV. THE GEEZER'S IN STIR — ROGER THE DODGER'S GOT BIRD — AND I'LL BET YOU'VE GOT RID OF THE FLAT MAN FOR GOOD, NOW! *

BUT... WHO CAN TELL? A DETECTIVE NEVER KNOWS WHAT CASE MAY BREAK...WHAT TERRIFIED VICTIM MAY WALK THROUGH THE DOOR...WHAT BIT OF INFORMATION MAY SEND HIM OFF UPON A NEW (AND POSSIBLY DANGEROUS) ADVENTURE.FOR INSTANCE AT THIS VERY MOMENT...

* Detective Language

Villain—a criminal
Stir—in prison
Bird—a prison sentence
Gone straight—now honest, stopped commiting crimes.

Police Reports

P.C. BEAVER REPORTS SUSPECT CAR Nº XQ 0011. SAME TIME EVERY FRIDAY AT BANK OPENING TIME JOHN SMITH (DRIVER) CRO 734/62

All policemen make reports on the information they gather. They clip or 'spike' the reports together, for the person who collects them (known as the collator).

Bulletin

The collator puts all the reports into a kind of news-sheet. Then each policeman can find out what is happening all over his area.

STATEMENT

LOST ALSATIAN

A cereal packet makes an excellent box file. Just be sure to label it with your name along one side, as shown.

Notebook

WRITE ON EVERY LINE AND LEAVE NO SPACES.

Always carry a notebook. Tie on a pencil with some string, like this. Use it to write down useful information.

For example, make notes of suspicious things, like a car always parked by a bank just at closing time. And try taking statements from people who have seen accidents. Remember—a policeman's notebook may be used in court as evidence. There must be no rubbing out. Each page must be numbered. Leave no gaps in the writing, even for paragraphs.

Reading Clues

What is the Story of the Fuzzville Heiress?

A clue is anything that helps you discover new information. It may be very small—a thread, a hair, a shiny screw on an old car number plate. A good detective can get lots of information from tiny details. Try this puzzle to test your skill at reading clues.

Shamus has just learned that a Fuzzville woman may be the long-lost heiress to the Wozinsky fortune. Where did the fortune come from? Why didn't she know about it sooner?

The pictures in the magazine show several clues to the Fuzzville woman's story. Study them carefully, noticing things like flags and buildings. (There is one clue you will find in almost every picture.)

Try to work out the story the pictures tell. Turn the page upside-down to find the answer.

Answer

Olga was the only child of the Wozinskys, a wealthy Russian family. (Notice the flag and jewels in the first picture.) Their lives were threatened by a revolution in Russia. Olga's mother, disguised as a peasant, asked a visiting English army officer to protect Olga. When she heard his train was wrecked she believed Olga had died.

He adopted Olga, not realizing who she really was—until her diamond brooch was recognized as possibly linking her to the Wozinskys and their fortune.

Examining a Witness

A person who has witnessed a crime is often confused and panicky. At first, it may seem impossible to get any facts from him. One of your most important jobs is to calm him down—only then will he remember what he knows.

Always start by getting the main facts—the very simple things, like the time and place.

These facts will identify your witness if the case comes to court.

Day of the week
Date
Time
Place
Name of the witness
Address
Telephone number
Occupation

These are the most important things you need to know. Going through the list will help to calm your witness. Knowing the list will help you to keep cool.

Never rely on your memory— write down everything your witness says. (Here, Bill is taking notes while Shamus questions Olga).

Now go on to get a description of the case. Ask your witness how he heard of the case, or why he found himself at the scene. Ask him what action he took. Again, write it all down.

When you ask for a description of a place or person, your witness may not know where to start. Help him by asking questions, as Shamus does on the right.

Again, start with simple things like height and weight and get him to compare the person with himself or you. Whenever you can, use examples to jog his memory.

AT THIS MOMENT THE DOOR IS OPENED BY THE VERY WOMAN SHAMUS HAS JUST BEEN READING ABOUT... THE HEIRESS TO THE WOZINSKY FORTUNE.

PRINCESS OLGA!

OH PLEASE...I NEED YOUR HELP. SOMEONE'S AFTER MY INHERITANCE!

AND SHE DESCRIBES HER FEARS...

YOU MEAN THE WOZINSKY FORTUNE? BUT I UNDERSTOOD FROM THE MAGAZINE STORY THAT IT WAS STILL IN A BANK IN SWITZERLAND.

THAT'S TRUE...I CAN'T CLAIM IT UNTIL MY PASSPORT ARRIVES. AND WHAT IF SOMEONE STEALS THE VITAL DOCUMENT MY LAWYER GAVE ME? IT'S THE WOZINSKY'S FAMILY ALBUM, YOU SEE, AND THERE'S A PAGE WITH CHILDISH FINGERMARKS THAT SEEM TO BE IDENTICAL WITH MINE..!

OF COURSE! THE PROOF OF YOUR IDENTITY!

YES... AND I'M SO WORRIED. SINCE THAT STORY IN THE PICTURE NEWS I'VE BEEN CONSTANTLY PESTERED. A MAN CAME TODAY WHO SAID HE WAS FROM MY LAWYER, BUT I SAW HIM RIFLING MY BUREAU DRAWERS!

I KNOW HE'LL RETURN — I'M SURE OF IT. MAURICE HERE WAS SUSPICIOUS FROM THE START.

MAURICE?

YES, MAURICE HERE—MAURICE WAS *SO* UPSET.

CAN YOU DESCRIBE THE MAN? YOU HAD A GOOD LOOK AT HIM?

HEAVENS, NO... I WAS TOO CONCERNED WITH MAURICE. HE'S STILL OVERWROUGHT, POOR DARLING... HE HAS *SUCH A* SENSITIVE NATURE...

BUT DETECTIVE INSPECTOR SHAMUS HAS FACED THIS KIND OF THING BEFORE.

DEAR LADY, YOU REMEMBER MORE THAN YOU THINK. GO SLOWLY— TODAY IS THURSDAY, MAY 16TH. THE TIME WAS—

GRADUALLY, SHAMUS CALMS THE DISTRAUGHT PRINCESS... AND LITTLE BY LITTLE, PRECIOUS FACTS BEGIN TO COME TO LIGHT...

WHEN YOU ANSWERED THE DOOR, DID YOU LOOK UP INTO HIS FACE? OR DOWN?

NOW LET ME THINK. THERE WAS A CUT ON HIS CHIN— YES, I LOOKED UP.

SLOWLY, WITH INFINITE PATIENCE SHAMUS ESTABLISHES THAT THE VISITOR WAS TALL... VERY TALL. A LEAN, SCOWLING MAN WITH THICK, GREY HAIR...

YACKETY YACKETY YACKETY

AND...

YOU MENTIONED HANGING UP A HAT. COULD YOU DESCRIBE IT? WOULD YOU SAY IT WAS OLD?

NEW? — NO...

— YES!

BROWN? — OH NO!

GREY? — YES—

AND COME TO THINK OF IT, I HAD A QUICK PEEK AT THE LABEL—

THE MAN HAD WORN A BRAND-NEW HAT... SO LARGE IT MIGHT HAVE BEEN BOUGHT TO FIT OVER A THICK GREY WIG...

MOST INTERESTING! BUT LET US LOOK THROUGH THE FILES... PERHAPS YOU CAN IDENTIFY YOUR MAN.

AND TOMORROW, WE'LL GO TO THE BANK WITH THAT VALUABLE ALBUM AND THE DIAMOND.

CERTAINLY, INSPECTOR... CERTAINLY..!

LET'S MAKE A START, THEN!

AT FIRST GLANCE, NONE OF THE PHOTOGRAPHS ON FILE IN CRIMINAL RECORDS RESEMBLES THE MAN SEEN BY THE PRINCESS...SO SHAMUS BEGINS THE ARDUOUS TASK OF BUILDING AN IDENTIFIT PICTURE TO MATCH OLGA'S DESCRIPTION...

ALL I CAN SAY IS THAT HE HAD A LONG, NARROW FACE, JUTTING JAW, THIN, BEAKY NOSE, TINY EYES AND A VERY SMALL, MEAN MOUTH..

AS THE PICTURE TAKES SHAPE, A DARK SUSPICION GROWS IN SHAMUS' MIND. BUT AS HE PONDERS THE PROBLEM HE MAY BE FACING, OLGA SLIPS AWAY.

COULD IT BE...THE FLAT MAN?

I REFUSE TO GIVE UP THE DIAMOND. I CAN HIDE IT... IN A VERY SAFE PLACE..!

How Identification Kits Work

The identification kit used by police works by building up layers of see-through photographs. Each shows just one feature, such as the chin or nose. It is chosen to match what the witness remembers. The layers can be slid up and down to change the face even more, as the witness remembers details.

In a photofit kit there may be hundreds of chins or noses to choose from, so they are sorted into groups. For example, there may be groups of square jaws or long noses. There are groups of close-together eyes, as well as eyes of different shapes, sizes and colours. There are also lots of different hats and hair styles.

But even one set of features can make several faces, if you squash them close or pull them far apart. Try making the kit shown here, and see what happens when you juggle the bits around. If you have read Olga's description in the story above, you may find a picture of the Flat Man . . . .

Hair and Features

Is this the Man?

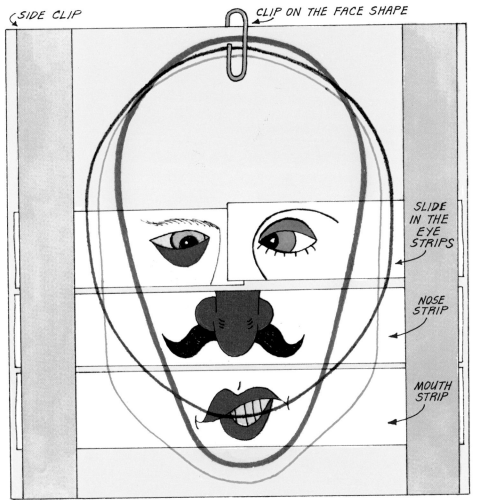

SIDE CLIP

CLIP ON THE FACE SHAPE

SLIDE IN THE EYE STRIPS

NOSE STRIP

MOUTH STRIP

Identi-Fit Kit

You will need
white card
thin paper or tracing paper
strips of stiff paper for the side clips
scissors, glue, pencil and rubber
four or five paper clips

Cut out a piece of card like the one shown on the left. Cut two strips of stiff paper, about 2cm wide and 4cm longer than the square. These are the side clips.

Glue one end of each side clip to the back of the card. When the glue is dry, fold round and glue the other end, pulling it tight. Hold it in place with a paper clip.

To make a face shape, trace the red outline on to a piece of paper about as big as the card. Trace the green and blue outlines separately to make two more shapes. Then trace the bits shown below on strips of paper at least as wide as the card and about 2cm deep.

To use the kit, clip a face shape over the square and try out different features by sliding them under the side clips. Trace over the whole face on a fresh piece of tracing paper to make a record for your criminal files.

Each of these coloured lines is the outline of a face. Trace the one that seems most like the face Olga describes. Trace some noses, mouths and eyes from the bits shown below, and try them on the face. Then turn the page to check your identifit against a genuine picture of the Flat Man.

HAT SHAPES

FOLLOWING HIS HUNCH SHAMUS RIFLES QUICKLY THROUGH HIS FILES...

IT MUST BE HIM...

AND SOON FINDS WHAT HE'S BEEN SEARCHING FOR...

PRINCESS! I THINK WE'VE GOT YOUR MAN!

SHE'S GONE, GUV... SLIPPED OUT TEN MINUTES AGO. SAID SOMETHING ABOUT DIN-DINS FOR DARLING MAURICE.

NO! WE'VE GOT TO CONTACT HER...THAT FLAT MAY BE FULL OF FINGERPRINTS.

WHILE HIS ASSISTANT CONTACTS THE PRINCESS, SHAMUS PACES THE OFFICE RESTLESSLY...

IT'S O.K., GUV — SHE HASN'T TOUCHED A THING. SAYS YOU'RE TO COME OVER AND JUST WALK IN. SHE'S LEFT THE DOOR ON THE LATCH!

SHE'S WHAT? HOLY MATILDA. HE MAY BE THERE ALREADY!

SHE DOESN'T SEEM TO REALIZE WHO WE MAY BE DEALING WITH.

GREAT SNAKES... THE FLAT MAN!

AND LEAPING INTO HIS FAITHFUL CAR, OLD SUSIE, SHAMUS SPEEDS TO THE FLAT.

WILL HE BE TOO LATE?

Keeping Records

As soon as you start working on a case, start keeping records. For example, when you are questioning a witness, you or an assistant should take notes. They may help show if the witness is confused, or lying. When the witness has remembered all he can, he should write a statement, as shown here.

Keep all your notes, papers and evidence together in a box file. Label each item with the case number. Remember, it's important to have all the details at your finger-tips.

Writing a Statement

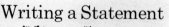

Taken by D.S. Wm. WATSON at Fuzzville Police Station between 4·10 and 4·45 on Wednesday 9/9/77

SAMPLE STATEMENT

In a statement, the witness should write down exactly what he knows about the case and sign his name, leaving no spaces where words could be added later. Sign your name, too.

Using Case Numbers

FUZZVILLE DIV. 6
CRIME 601/77

SAMPLE LABEL FOR EVIDENCE

If your first case turns up in 1979, its case number will be 1/79. Give each case its own number and use this number on all reports, papers and evidence.

12

Criminal Records

What Shamus has just found is the Flat Man's criminal record —the papers that describe him and give details of all his criminal activities. Here is the first page.

A record like this is started for each criminal as soon as he is arrested. You can use this form as a model for your own files—just copy the printed part. Page 16 tells how to take fingerprints.

Every suspect is given a number when he is first arrested. This is shown on all his records. The number here shows that the Flat Man was the 883rd criminal in Fuzzville (FV) and was first convicted in 1957.

CRIMINAL RECORD

CRO FV 883/57

883/57   883/57

NAME: Weedy Weeky (BELIEVED FALSE)
ALIAS(ES): The Flat Man
D.O.B.: August 23 1937
OCCUPATION: Pilot, Racing Driver
DESCRIPTION:
HEIGHT: 6'3"   BUILD: Slim   HAIR: Black (Dyed)
EYES: Grey   COMPLEXION: Sallow   MARKS: Scars

FINGERPRINTS
LEFT HAND

THUMB   1   2   3   4

PRINTS TAKEN BY INEXPERIENCED OFFICER... SMUDGED BECAUSE TOO MUCH INK WAS USED

RIGHT HAND

THUMB   1   2   3   4

HABITS

PROPERTY: Gold Pencil, Crowbar, Sausage
COURT: Fuzzville Mansi
DETAILS CIRCULATED

More Detective Language

Alias—false name
Charge—the particular crime or offence for which the criminal was arrested.
D.O.B.—date of birth

M.O.—(Modus Operandi) the way a particular criminal works. A criminal usually sticks to the same kind of crime and does it the same way. If he lies, he usually sticks to the same story.

The M.O. may help a detective to identify him.
Property—things the criminal was carrying, or things in his pockets when arrested.

Searching for Fingerprints

The skin of your fingertips has a pattern of ridges which is special for each person. If you press them on an ink pad and then on paper, you can see the print left by these ridges. The oily sweat on your skin can print the patterns, too. It leaves good prints on polished things like glass or silver—though you need a fingerprint kit to see the details. (The next pages show you how to make one.)

Fingerprints can help you work out who has been at the scene of a crime—but there are tricks to searching for them.

First, when you search a room be careful not to leave your own prints. Avoid touching anything, even the door, with your fingertips. Do not think it will be safe if you wear gloves—this can make you careless. Gloved fingers can smudge good prints, and a split in the glove may let the fingerprint through. (This happens to criminals, too.)

Stop and look about when you enter the room. Then search it carefully and thoroughly. Go over it in a circle (clockwise or anti-clockwise) to make sure you've covered every spot. Make notes of all the places where you see finger-shaped smudges, or where you guess you might find prints. Later you can use your fingerprint kit to develop them (make them show up) and put them in your files.

Follow Detective Shamus round this picture to see how and where to look for fingerprints. Move anti-clockwise, along the path shown by the arrows.

14

Print-Hunting Practice

A normal fingerprint is just a delicate grease-mark. Usually it takes a slanting light to show it up. You may get the right light by stooping and bending your head, but often you need to pick things up.

Practise examining things without using your fingertips. Use tweezers to lift small things and use a pencil to open and close drawers. Always start at the bottom and work up—then you needn't close each drawer to examine the next one.

To lift a cup or glass, put your fingers inside, as Shamus does. Then open your hand so that it presses against the sides. (Be sure to practise on a plastic cup or tumbler!)

Be careful to touch things as little as possible. Notice how Shamus uses rulers to close a window. The only point touched is the inside corner of the frame—a place where you would never find a print. You can use this trick to open a window too. Always push into the corner—not straight up or down—and push both corners.

With practice you will find lots of ways to move things without touching them. Pencils and tweezers are useful, but you may want to invent your own tools too—like loops of wire, or hooks for lifting things.

Work with a friend to exchange ideas and have contests. Go round a room together and see who is the first to find a fingerprint in each part of it.

Keep in mind the likely spots, like T.V. knobs and light switches. Smooth, polished things show the best prints.

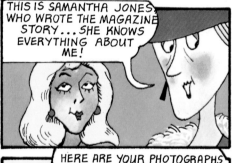

Comic panel text:

FOR AN INSTANT, A FAMILIAR SILHOUETTE FLICKERS IN THE LIGHTS OF A PASSING CAR. BUT AS SHAMUS LEANS OUT INTO THE DARKNESS, THE DOORBELL RINGS...

BRRRR

AND HE TURNS TO SEE PRINCESS OLGA WITH A STRANGER...

INSPECTOR, MEET MY NEW FRIEND!

THIS IS SAMANTHA JONES WHO WROTE THE MAGAZINE STORY... SHE KNOWS EVERYTHING ABOUT ME!

HERE ARE YOUR PHOTOGRAPHS BUT YOU NEVER GAVE ME THE ALBUM.

OH, I PROMISED NOT TO LET IT GO. WE'RE GOING TO POP IT SAFELY IN THE BANK TOMORROW MORNING AREN'T WE, INSPECTOR?

FUZZVILLE BANK?

YES... JUST UNTIL I GO TO SWITZERLAND.

SHAMUS RETURNS TO WORK FEELING TROUBLED BY THIS INTERRUPTION. BUT THERE IS A JOB TO DO... HE FEELS SURE THAT SOMEWHERE IN THIS ROOM HE WILL FIND A TELL-TALE FINGERPRINT...

Fingerprint Kit

Here is what you need for a fingerprint kit. Notice the special powders used to develop prints. Use them when you search for fingerprints.

For practice, try developing your own prints. First rub your fingertips in your hair to make them oily. Then press them firmly on white paper. Use pencil powder to develop them.

Use pencil lead to make dark powder. First, grind off as much wood as possible. Then, holding the pencil over some paper, carefully grind just the tip. Press it gently against the blade of the sharpener. Pour the powder into a container – you only need a bit.

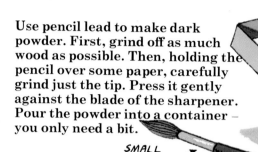

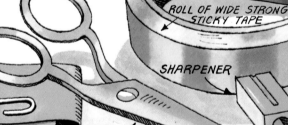

STAMP PAD

SMALL CLEAN DRY PAINTBRUSH

LEAD PENCIL

ROLL OF WIDE STRONG STICKY TAPE

SHARPENER

PAINT PAD

SCISSORS

ENVELOPES TO HOLD POWDERS. FOLD SEVERAL TIMES AND FASTEN WITH PAPERCLIPS

PRINTS ON FILE
Elmer T. Bloggs
Aliases used: NONE
LEFT HAND
THUMB   1   2   3   4

To take a print, first 'ink' the finger on a stamp or paint pad, rolling it from side to side. Then press it firmly on the album and roll it from side to side again. Label each set of prints as shown.

When you find prints, you can develop them, lift them and put them in the album. Label to show when and where you found them.

Make an album from a scrapbook. Start by taking prints from all your family—then search for prints to develop and compare. The next pages show how to examine them.

If you don't have a stamp pad, make a paint pad. Use a piece of soft cloth, folded several times. Pour on thick poster paint until the pad is soaked. To take a print, press the finger very lightly on the pad and roll it from side to side.

ECT PRINTS
d time: 10·00am APRIL 26ᵀᴴ 1978
c:- TOP AND SIDES OF T.V. SET IN FRONT LIVING ROOM IN HOME OF DOCTOR WEIGHT, 48 HOLMES DRIVE, CAMBRIDGE.

WHERE DISCOVERED ON T.V.

FINGERPRINT ALBUM

MAGNIFYING GLASS

1 Developing Prints

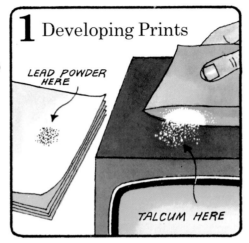

LEAD POWDER HERE

TALCUM HERE

Use talcum powder on dark things and pencil lead on light things. Dip the brush in and gently shake off any extra powder.

2

Brush the powder very lightly from side to side over the spot where you expect to find a print. Be sure to cover a fairly big area.

3

Clean the brush by blowing it or wiping with a tissue. Then carefully brush the loose powder away from the print.

1 Lifting Prints

PRESS FIRMLY

Unroll a length of tape and press it carefully on to the developed print. Then cut the tape.

2

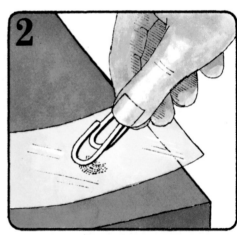

Press down hard on the print and rub it well with your fingernail or a paper clip. This brings the pattern of powder on to the tape.

3

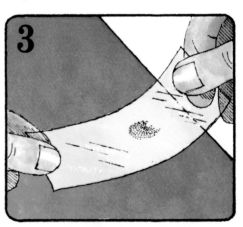

If you peel off the tape carefully, the print will come up, too. You will see it again when you stick the tape down again. Always stick talcum prints on darkish paper.

Examining Fingerprints

A fingerprint is one of the most deadly clues a criminal can leave.

First of all, each fingerprint is unique. The tiny ridges of skin on a fingertip make a pattern that is different from any other in the world. Even identical twins have different fingerprints.

Second, your fingerprints never change. No matter how old you become, no matter how well disguised you are, your prints reveal your true identity.

Some criminals have tried to burn away their prints, but when the skin grew back, the patterns came to light again . . . .

Try examining some fingerprints yourself—the main shapes of fingerprints are shown below. On the right, you can see how Detective Shamus examines the prints left by the Flat Man in Princess Olga's flat. Could you identify the Flat Man's fingerprints? The puzzle at the bottom of the page is a chance to try.

ARCH

This pattern is called an arch, because the shape in the middle is like an arch. The ridges round it are arch-shaped too.

LOOP

The centre line in a loop is shaped a bit like a hairpin. When you find a loop, you will always find another shape called a delta. The ridges repeat until they get to the delta.

Matching Fingerprints

Take prints of your family and sort them into groups like these—arches, loops, whorls and mixed. (Police files use these groups.) Then find and develop a print from somewhere in your house. See if you can work out whose it is.

Get paper and pencil for taking notes, a metal pointer or sharp pencil for counting ridges and, if you can, a magnifying glass that magnifies 2 times.

Now go to work on the subject print like this:

1. Decide which group the print belongs in (arch, whorl, loop or mixed).
2. Check for identifying marks like cuts and scars.
3. Match the deltas, or any other small shapes you notice.
4. Count the lines (or ridges) between these shapes, to see if the number is the same.

When counting, always start at the centre shape and work outwards until you reach a new shape or odd-looking ridge. Make a quick sketch of it. Then go back to the centre and work outwards in a new direction. Always follow a pattern (clockwise or anti-clockwise) and keep notes as you work. The notes might look like this:

1. Whorl.
2. Small cut lower left.
3. 34 lines between right-hand edge of whorl and the next shape. (Draw the shape.)

WHORL

A pattern with a line that curls up in the middle is called a whorl. It may be circular or long. It always has two deltas, one each side.

MIXED

There are many kinds of mixtures. One of the commonest is a double-loop. The line right in the centre bends back upon itself.

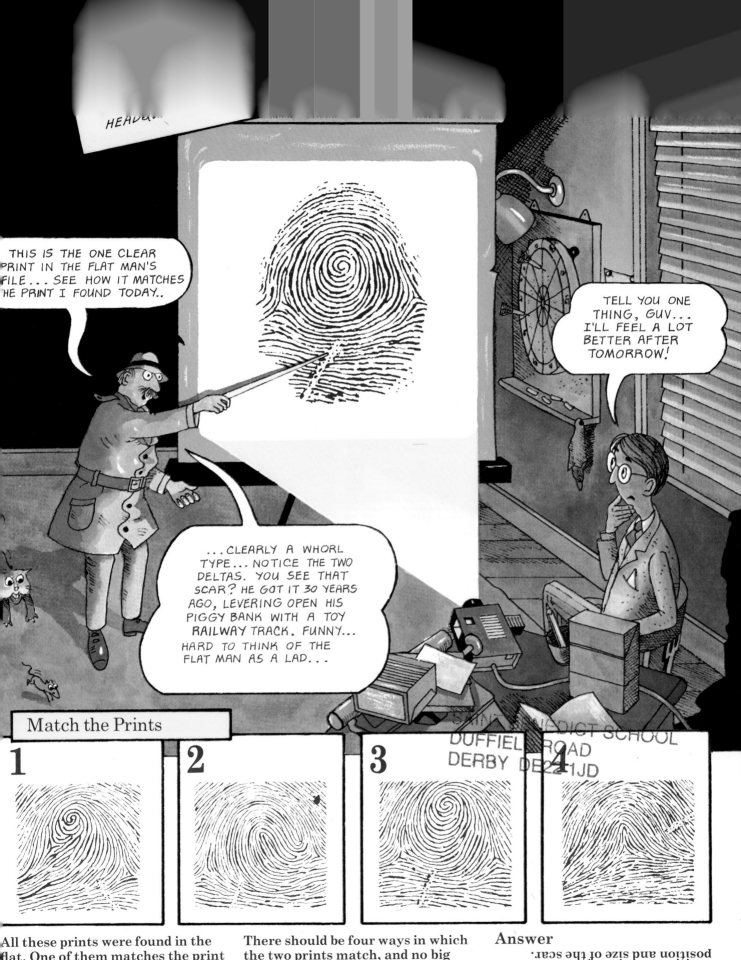

Match the Prints

1 **2** **3** **4**

All these prints were found in the flat. One of them matches the print from the Flat Man's file, shown above. Can you find it?

There should be four ways in which the two prints match, and no big differences. (Turn the page upside-down to see the answer.)

Answer

No. 3 matches. Notice the whorl, the position of each delta, and the position and size of the scar.

Police Escort

Police are often asked to protect valuable things or Very Important People (sometimes called V.I.P.s) as they are taken from place to place. This is called an 'escort'. The police stay close to the V.I.P., ready to shield him from attack and get him clear of danger.

It may take years of practice to get a feel for all the places where danger might be lurking, and the kinds of ordinary-looking event which may really be the start of a clever attack. However, it will help if you remember these main points:

1. Two people make a good escort team—one to walk just ahead of the V.I.P., one behind.
2. Be specially cautious at corners and points where you can't see the route ahead.
3. Steer clear of possible hiding places like doorways.
4. Stay alert at all times.

Escort Practice

For escort practice, you need at least three people. One is the detective, one is the criminal, and one is the V.I.P.

Pin some paper to the V.I.P.'s shoulder to make a target. The criminal needs a felt pen to mark the target with. Plan a route with start and finish points. Give the criminal five minutes to hide himself along the route. Then as the escort walks past, the criminal tries to mark the V.I.P.'s paper badge. The detective can stop him by shouting 'Criminal Alert!' before he strikes. He must hide again after each try, whether he strikes or is caught. (This can be a game if you take turns. The detective whose V.I.P. gets the least shoulder marks from Start to Finish is the winner.)

Call-Up

As a detective, there may be times when you need help fast. This is when you use a radio call-up.

Every policeman has a two-way radio which links him to radio control (the operator shown in the centre, below). With the flick of a switch, he can use his radio to contact control. If he says 'Emergency!' control stops all other calls to take his message.

Control can broadcast calls for help to every police radio in the area.

Your radio calls should be short and clear. Begin with the code for control (FV for Fuzzville) and give your number or name and rank. For instance, 'FV from 663, a message, 663 over.' (The word 'over' means you have finished speaking.) In a crisis, start by saying 'emergency'.

When spelling names or giving car numbers, it may be hard to say the letters clearly. Use the international call-up alphabet shown on the right. In this, an easy-to-hear word stands for each letter.

Call-Up Alphabet

A — Alpha	N — November
B — Bravo	O — Oscar
C — Charlie	P — Papa
D — Delta	Q — Quebec
E — Echo	R — Rome
F — Foxtrot	S — Sierra
G — Golf	T — Tango
H — Hotel	U — Uncle
I — India	V — Victor
J — Juliet	W — Whisky
K — Kilo	X — Xray
L — Lima	Y — Yankee
M— Mike	Z — Zebra

Using this alphabet, the car number 'JFB 3H' is 'Juliet Foxtrot Bravo 3 Hotel'.

Know Your Scene

You must know your neighbourhood thoroughly to set up a road-block. You must know the times and places where traffic might be heavy and where the criminals might slip the net (like motorway entrances). You must know every one-way road and short-cut, to plan where your team should be waiting.

Once a call-up starts, you should be able to seal off the area in minutes.

Unfortunately, experienced criminals expect this—and plan for it. A criminal usually tries to dump his getaway car, and switch to a different kind of car or transport, before he hits the road-block.

But the abandoned car may hold a vital clue, like a set of fingerprints—or it may help pinpoint the criminal's whereabouts. The sooner you find it, the more useful it is.

When you are searching for a getaway car, try to put yourself into the criminal's place. What do you think his final destination is—a river, an airport, a motorway? What dangers must he avoid, like crowds and traffic? Where might he find a spot to switch his car without being seen?

A good map of your neighbourhood is all-important. Below you can see how to prepare it.

Preparing a Map

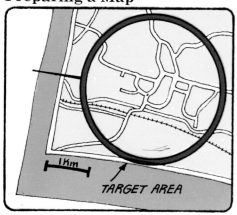

First get a street plan of your area. Try the local library, a bus station or an estate agent's. Mark in red the main target for criminal attack —the bank or the jeweller.

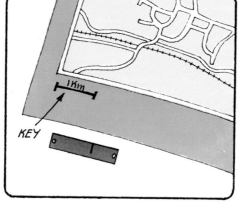

Use the 'key' or 'legend' in the corner of the map to measure a strip of cardboard that stands for 2 km. Make a small hole at each end of the strip.

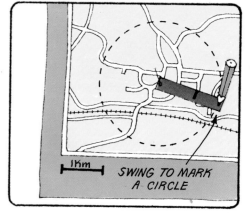

Stick a pin through one hole in to the 'target' area. Stick a pencil through the other hole. Swing it to make a circle. This shows where your road-block should be set up.

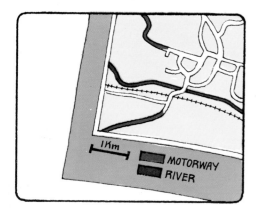

Use coloured pencils to mark points the criminals might head for, like motorways, rivers and roads that lead to airports. Then glue the map to a piece of card.

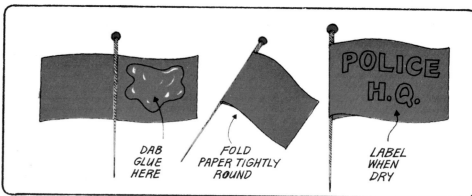

Make flags, like these, to mark all the spots you may need to know in an emergency—like your local hospital, police and fire stations. Mark all the phone boxes—you never know when you'll need one.

Then search your neighbourhood for spots to dump a getaway car, like old yards and warehouses. Look for taxi-ranks or railway stations; the criminal may need them if his car-swap fails. Mark these, too.

Find the Getaway Car

Now that the alarm has been given, the Fuzzville police are looking for the Maserooni J8. They have a description of the car and the criminals and the car number plate. In any case, a Maserooni is hard to miss. But this, of course, is part of the Flat Man's plan.

Like all experienced criminals, the Flat Man knows he must dump his getaway car very fast. Knowing the car will have been spotted, heading east for the M10, he is now heading back towards the bank.

Below you can see the area inside the road-block. Somewhere in this area the Flat Man must get rid of the Maserooni and begin the next stage of his getaway. Can you work out where and how he will do it? (Page 32 shows the answer.)

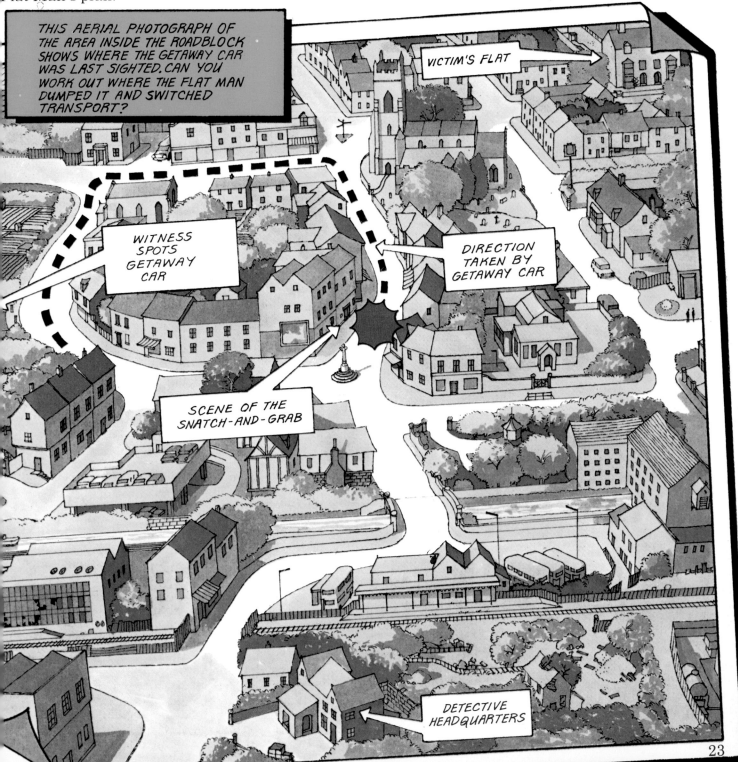

THIS AERIAL PHOTOGRAPH OF THE AREA INSIDE THE ROADBLOCK SHOWS WHERE THE GETAWAY CAR WAS LAST SIGHTED. CAN YOU WORK OUT WHERE THE FLAT MAN DUMPED IT AND SWITCHED TRANSPORT?

VICTIM'S FLAT

WITNESS SPOTS GETAWAY CAR

DIRECTION TAKEN BY GETAWAY CAR

SCENE OF THE SNATCH-AND-GRAB

DETECTIVE HEADQUARTERS

Using Clues

Even the most experienced criminal often gives himself away by tiny clues left at the scene of the crime. Some clues may give you a good idea of who (or where) the criminal is. (This is called a 'lead'.) Clues may also be used as evidence (to help prove your case in a law court.)

Anything the criminal left or marked or disturbed may turn out to be an important clue—if you know how to use it. Keep each clue in a plastic bag and label it. (The police make plaster casts of things like teethmarks and footprints.) Follow Bill round the laboratory on the right to see some of the ways science can help.

POLICE PHOTOGRAPH TAKEN AT THE SCENE OF THE CRIME

Find the Clues

The villains who snatched Olga's valuables have left at least four clues at the scene of the crime. Can you find them?

Answers

1. Wig (one of the criminal's hairs may have stuck to it)
2. Cap (same reason—the criminal may have worn it on his real hair)
3. Footprint (see below on what footprints can show
4. Plank (see what the plank shows on the right)

Reading Footprints

To get clues from footprints, you need to study how they are made. Practice with several pairs of shoes, like those shown below. Try to work with friends who are bigger, smaller or a different weight, so you can compare prints and test each other.

Work on damp sand or fine, damp earth and rake or smooth it before you start. Be very careful not to pack it down.

First walk on it normally, in different pairs of shoes. Measure each sole and compare it to its print. Then try running and limping in the same shoes and see where the shoe presses down. Try a standing jump to see where your toes dig in. Notice what happens if you are carrying a heavy load.

Notice that a new shoe may print the maker's name or trademark. This may help you solve a case.

The maker of the shoes will have a list of stockists (shops that sell his shoes). You can go round to the nearby stockists and question them. If you know the brand and size, a shop assistant may still remember the people who bought them. This could help narrow down your list of suspects.

Remember, even the size of the print may tell you something important about who made it.

Compare these Shoes and Shoe-Prints

HIGH HEEL   SHOE WITH HEEL   SMOOTH-SOLED SANDAL   RUNNING SHOE   WALKING BOOT   GUM BOOT

OLD SHOE WITH WORN HEEL AND SOLE   SMALL NEW SHOE   LARGE NEW SHOE   NOTICE HOW THE SHAPE CHANGES AS THE SHOE GETS OLD.   SMALL OLD SHOE   LARGE OLD SHOE   SMALL NEW SHOE   LARGE NEW SHOE

AS SHAMUS DIRECTS OPERATIONS AT THE SCENE OF THE SNATCH, HE KEEPS IN TOUCH WITH RADIO CONTROL. AT LAST...

THEY GOT AWAY, GUV... WE FOUND THE CAR. THEIR BOILER SUITS WERE INSIDE.

I'LL TAKE A LOOK AT THE GETAWAY CAR... YOU TAKE THIS LOT TO THE LAB, BILL.

IN FUZZVILLE'S FORENSIC SCIENCE LABORATORY...

RUSH JOB I'M AFRAID!

AGAIN? YOUR GOVERNOR SENT SOME PACKETS FROM THE FLAT LAST NIGHT.

RIGHT, LADS... PRIORITY CRIME. STOP EVERYTHING AND START ON THIS LOT!

HAVE YOU GOT ANYTHING FROM LAST NIGHT?

OH YES... THE LADS HAVE BEEN BUSY.

FANCY A SANDWICH?

WE GOT A GOOD CAST OF THE BITES.

PLASTER CAST

THE TEETHMARKS ARE DEFINITELY THE FLAT MAN'S. H'MMM... CLEVER OF SHAMUS TO SPOT HIS M.O.!*

FLAT MAN'S DENTAL CHART

*M.O. — MODUS OPERANDI (THE FLAT MAN IS A NERVOUS NIBBLER.)

BILL WATCHES EAGERLY AS THE WORK BEGINS...

AS THE CRIMINAL'S CAP IS CAREFULLY UNSTITCHED (A HAIR COULD BE INSIDE.)

AS THE WIG IS EXAMINED FOR ANY LOOSE HAIRS THAT MAY BELONG TO THE CRIMINAL...

AS EACH HAIR IS MOUNTED BETWEEN GLASS SLIDES, TO GO UNDER A MICROSCOPE...

AND EVEN THE PLANK IS THOROUGHLY CHECKED...

LOOK AT THIS SMEAR OF PAINT. I'LL BET IT'S MEANT TO HIDE SOMETHING!

UNDER AN ULTRA-VIOLET LAMP, THE NAME OF A BUILDER'S YARD SHOWS BENEATH THE PAINT...

MUST BE SOME **REASON** WHY IT WAS PAINTED OUT. ANOTHER LEAD..?

AT LAST, BILL RETURNS TO H.Q. WITH THE REPORTS. BUT HIS DAY ISN'T OVER YET...

Come to Olga's flat there's been a break-in Shamus

The Scene of the Crime

Try to keep calm when you face the confusion left at the scene of a crime. A lot may depend on what you notice and what you do. Keep these rules in mind.

1 Look First—Don't Touch

Don't touch anything until the scene has been examined and dusted for fingerprints.

2 Follow a Method

Make your examination step-by-step. Look for fingerprints first. Use your kit to pick up any prints you find. Then, slowly circle the room again. Look for anything the criminal might have touched or left.

3 Use Your Notebook

Write down everything interesting you see. Don't leave out any detail that might be useful. Remember that what you notice and write down may be used as evidence.

4 Clues and Evidence

The next page shows tips on gathering evidence.

5 Take Full Statements

Ask victims and witnesses to tell you everything they can (see page 8) and write it down. Take the full name and address of any person mentioned.

Remember, it may be a long time until your case goes to court. Your notebook must give a complete picture of what happened today.

6 Search Thoroughly

Now it doesn't matter if you disturb things. Look everywhere —even in dustbins and drain-pipes—for anything the criminal might have left. (Even the stub of a train ticket might give you an important lead.)

7 Work out a Story

From the start, try to work out what happened, to get an idea of what to look for.

Collecting Evidence

Which ball broke the window? The position of the evidence may give you a clue. (Check your answer on page 32).

BALL Nº 1
2M. FROM DOOR
1·8M. FROM NORTH WALL.

BALL Nº 2
2·7M. FROM EAST WALL.
3·5M. S.W. OF TREE.

BROKEN GLASS SCATTERED AS FAR AS 1M. INSIDE OF DOOR.

2 Put each piece of evidence in a plastic bag. Don't touch it—use tweezers. Or push it on to some card, then into the bag.

3 Label the bag to show the case-number and your name. Later you can examine the evidence more thoroughly.

Before you remove the evidence, take a photograph or make a sketch to show where you found it. The exact position may be vital.

Give at least two measurements, as shown, to pinpoint a position. Measure from things, like walls or trees, that stay in the same spot.

Label the bag to show the case-number and your name. Later you can examine the evidence more thoroughly.

SAFE?

I NEVER DREAMED THEY'D LOOK UNDER THE MATTRESS!

WELL, THE STORY'S CLEAR ENOUGH! WHILE THE PRINCESS WAS HELPING US AT H.Q. THEY ABANDONED THE GETAWAY CAR, BROKE INTO THE FLAT, AND GOT THE DIAMOND. THE EARTH UNDER THE WINDOW IS COVERED WITH FOOTPRINTS. AND WE FOUND A TRACE OF PAINT ON THE CARPET. IF MY HUNCH IS RIGHT IT'LL TIE IN WITH THIS MORNING'S JOB!

BUT WE KNOW IT'S THE FLAT MAN... DON'T WE?

I'M NOT SO SURE, JUST TAKE A LOOK AT THIS!

BUT THIS IS AMATEUR STUFF! *THIS* LOT OF DRAWERS WAS OPENED TOP TO BOTTOM... THE FLAT MAN DOESN'T OPERATE LIKE THAT.

RIGHT! AND THE PRINCESS CLAIMS THAT CLOTHES ARE MISSING. NOTICE THE OPENED PERFUME BOTTLES... LONG BLONDE HAIR IN THE COMB... AND UNDER THE LEFT-HAND SET OF DRAWERS WE FOUND...

...THIS!

BLOOD!

NO, PRINCESS! A BIT OF BROKEN FINGERNAIL... WITH BLOOD-RED VARNISH!

IF IT'S THE FLAT MAN, HE MUST HAVE AN ACCOMPLICE! WE KNOW IT'S AN AMATEUR, AND PROBABLY A WOMAN.

BUT WHO? AND WHY?

Interpol

Many dangerous criminals roam from country to country in their search for riches—and their flight from detection. They try to escape to places where they are unknown.

They can only be stopped if the police of different countries band together, exchanging help and information. This is the purpose of the International Criminal Police Organization—known as Interpol.

Over 100 countries belong to Interpol. Each country is ready to share its information with the rest and take up the hunt when a criminal is thought to have crossed its borders. Each helps pay for special services like news bulletins and telephone links.

Interpol has its headquarters in Paris. It has its own laboratories to test for counterfeits and forgeries. Once a year it holds a meeting, where police sent from each country discuss crime problems shared by all.

But Interpol does its most vital work through its telex and telephone services. In minutes they can link police a thousand miles apart—and start tightening the net around a criminal.

MEANWHILE, AT FUZZVILLE DETECTIVE HEADQUARTERS...

WHOEVER THE VILLAINS ARE THEY'LL SOON BE HEADING FOR SWITZERLAND TO CLAIM THE FORTUNE. WE'VE GOT TO STOP THEM.

INTERPOL!

RIGHT AGAIN, OLD BILL. GET ME PARIS HEADQUARTERS.

WITHIN MINUTES A CALL GOES OUT FROM LONDON TO PARIS...

THEN FROM PARIS TO EVERY COUNTRY ON THE SWISS BORDER. SOON THE POLICE OF EACH COUNTRY HAVE A DESCRIPTION OF THE CRIMINALS.

WHILE THE FAMOUS OLD SWISS BANK THAT GUARDS THE WOZINSKY FORTUNE IS IMMEDIATELY PUT ON THE ALERT.

SHAMUS HIMSELF WARNS THE MANAGER OF THE SWISS BANK...

BE ON YOUR GUARD FOR IMPOSTERS!

BUT, MONSIEUR SHAMUS, I HAVE JUST HAD A CALL FROM PRINCESS OLGA. SHE IS ARRIVING TOMORROW MORNING AT 11.00.

THIS IS SERIOUS...IT MUST BE THE FLAT MAN'S ACCOMPLICE. SHE'LL BE STAKING HER CLAIM IN LESS THAN 15 HOURS.

OH! IT'S TOO DREADFUL! AND ONLY TODAY MY PASSPORT FINALLY ARRIVED!

BUT THAT'S A PIECE OF LUCK. YOU'RE COMING WITH US...TO SWITZERLAND.

THAT, NIGHT...

I TELL YOU, BILL... THIS TIME I'M GOING TO TRAP THEM.

YOU MEAN...A STAKE OUT?

Stake-Out

A stake-out is a police trap. It is set up when detectives know a certain target will be attacked. They plan things so that the villains can get into the trap without spotting the detectives —but can't get out.

Detectives near the target may be disguised as shop assistants or bank clerks. Those outside are disguised as shoppers, window-cleaners—even tramps. Hidden all round are unmarked police cars and motor bikes.

One detective acts as 'eyes'. Usually he watches from some point like an upper window. He radios news of the villain's movements to the other detectives and signals when it's time to spring the trap.

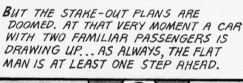

BY MID-MORNING THEY ARRIVE AT THE SWISS BANK...

DON'T BE LONG, BILL...JUST GIVE HIM A QUICK WALK ROUND THE BLOCK!

...WHERE THE MANAGER AWAITS THEM IN THE VAULTS.

THIS IS THE REAL PRINCESS!

SUCH ELEGANCE ...TRULY, HER BLUE BLOOD SHOWS!

WE HAVE ONLY AN HOUR TO PREPARE. WHEN THE IMPOSTER ARRIVES, PRETEND TO BELIEVE HER STORY. IT'S HER ACCOMPLICE I WANT... WE MUSTN'T SPRING THE TRAP 'TIL WE'VE GOT THEM BOTH!

BUT THE STAKE-OUT PLANS ARE DOOMED. AT THAT VERY MOMENT A CAR WITH TWO FAMILIAR PASSENGERS IS DRAWING UP...AS ALWAYS, THE FLAT MAN IS AT LEAST ONE STEP AHEAD.

IT'S THE SECURITY OFFICER. THE FAKE PRINCESS HAS ARRIVED!

QUICK...THE EMERGENCY STAIRS. WE'LL HAVE TO MANAGE WITHOUT OLD BILL!

THIS WAY, PRINCESS. WE'LL HIDE IN THE FOYER.

I AM OLGA... HEIRESS TO THE WOZINSKY FORTUNE.

DO YOU HAVE PROOF?

OF COURSE...THIS DIAMOND...AND THE OLD FAMILY ALBUM WITH MY FINGERPRINTS.

VERY GOOD! BUT WE MUST COMPARE YOUR FINGERPRINTS WITH THE ALBUM. A MERE FORMALITY...

AND SO...

PRINCESS OLGA CLAIMS THE WOZINSKY FORTUNE...

AND DEVOTES HERSELF TO REWARDING HER FAITHFUL COMPANION.

WON'T YOU HAVE JUST *ONE* MORE SAUSAGE, DARLING?

PERHAPS I CAN SELL THE STORY!

SAMANTHA JONES, FORMERLY OF THE PICTURE NEWS, IS JAILED FOR HER PART IN THE ATTEMPTED FRAUD.

AND D.I. SHAMUS AND D.C. WILLIAM WATSON TAKE UP THEIR DUTIES AGAIN AT FUZZVILLE POLICE H.Q.

WELL GUV, I GUESS IT'S BACK TO THE QUIET LIFE..!

I WONDER...

H'MMM..!

AS FOR THE NOTORIOUS WEEDY WEEKY (ALIAS 'THE FLAT MAN') WHO CAN TELL.....?

Did You Guess?

One of the people who knew most about Olga's claim to the fortune—who had an introduction to Olga and a chance to get hold of photographs to help forge identification papers—was the writer of the magazine story. This, as you may remember, was Samantha Jones.

The opportunity was immediately clear to the Flat Man, who read the story in the Picture News. He contacted Samantha and helped her plan the fraud. Through her friendship with Olga, he learned what he needed to know about Olga's plans and movements.

He helped Samantha steal the diamond and the old family album, so they could take out the page showing Olga's baby fingerprints—and put in a phoney page with Samantha's fingerprints. With these they could have claimed the fortune—if they had not been outwitted by D.I. Shamus.

Helping Police

Remember—information is the key to crime-fighting.

Practise describing people you see, making quick notes on their main features and what they wear. Learn to recognize different kinds of car and to memorize car numbers quickly.

Most important, learn how to telephone emergency services, like the police. If you see a crime or accident, phone the police immediately

DON'T TAKE RISKS— NEVER TRY TO STOP A CRIMINAL!

Answers

Page 23 The car-swap took place at the two-storey car park near the bank.

Page 27 The direction in which the broken glass fell shows that the window was probably broken by a ball thrown in from the garden when the door was closed.